TOTALLY BRAIN-BENDING PUZZLES

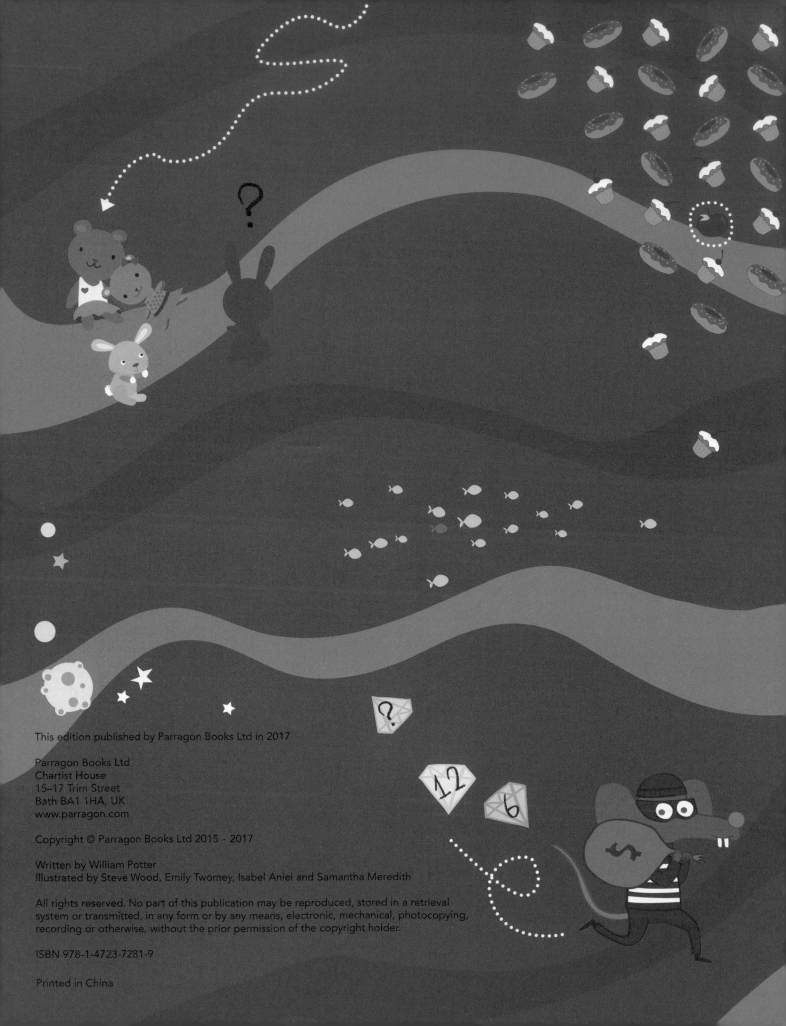

This edition published by Parragon Books Ltd in 2017

Parragon Books Ltd
Chartist House
15–17 Trim Street
Bath BA1 1HA, UK
www.parragon.com

Written by William Potter
Illustrated by Steve Wood, Emily Twomey, Isabel Aniel and Samantha Meredith

ISBN 978-1-4723-7281-9

Printed in China

TOTALLY BRAIN-BENDING PUZZLES

Over **100** incredibly **puzzling** activities

PaRragon

Bath • New York • Cologne • Melbourne • Delhi
Hong Kong • Shenzhen • Singapore

Tech teacher

The school computer has caught a virus! It keeps repeating letters. Cross out all the letters that there are more than one of to see today's subject.

C	O	Z	J	B	C	Z	O	J	Z
A	F	O	B	J	F	J	H	O	B
F	B	M	F	O	J	B	C	Z	O
J	Z	C	Z	B	Z	O	B	S	C
O	C	F	B	F	O	F	Z	O	Z
Z	B	J	O	T	Z	C	B	F	C

Today's lesson is

....

4

sleepy puppy

Dozy the dog is dreaming of his favourite part of the rug. See if you can find it!

Big brother, Little brother!

I'm Little Liam. Copy me one square at a time into the larger grid to see what my big brother Giant Jake looks like!

Tool trouble

Peter the plumber has dropped his spanners! How many of each colour are in the pile?

Green ▢

Orange ▢

Blue ▢

Pink ▢

Purple ▢

Maths Mystery

6 ☐ 6 = 12

15 ☐ 5 = 10

6 ☐ 3 = 9

12 ☐ 5 = 7

4 ☐ 3 = 7

Help me finish the sums by filling in the missing + and – signs.

Lost City

Follow the directions to discover the Lost Jungle City! Where is it on the map? Mark it by drawing an X.

1. From the Start, go up 4 squares.
2. Move 5 squares towards the Thorn Forest.
3. Go up 3 squares, then 2 squares right, then up 2 squares.
4. Go 2 squares towards the Pitless Bottom.
5. Move down 1 square, then left 4 squares.
6. Go down by 6 squares.
7. The Lost Jungle City is 4 squares right of here!

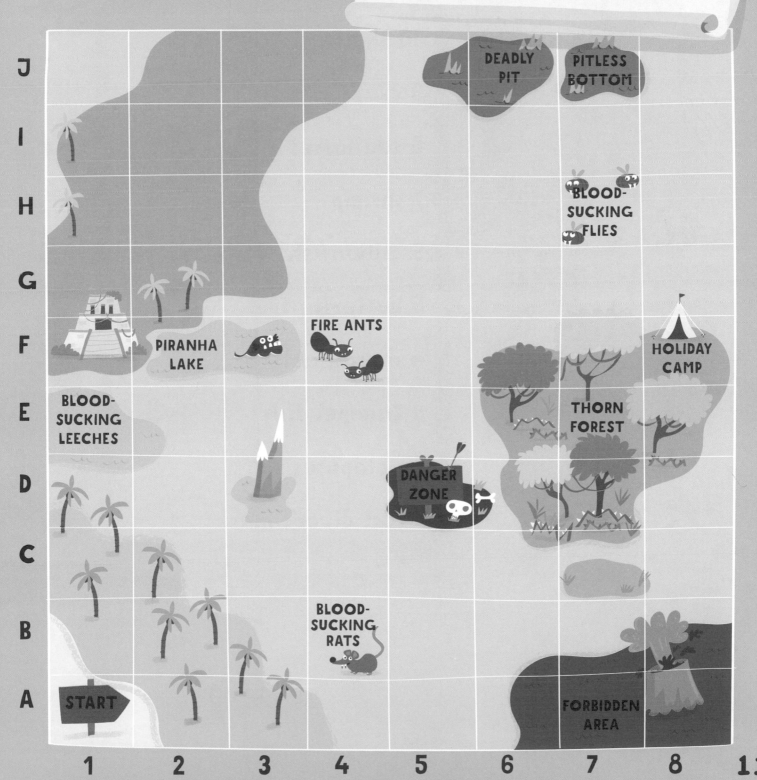

Ella is doing a survey of the coral reef...

Help her find:

10 shells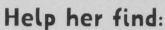

9 crabs

8 seahorses

7 shrimp

6 clownfish

5 butterfly fish

4 moray eels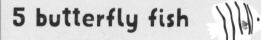

3 trumpet fish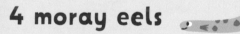

2 octopuses

1 lost diver's mask

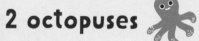

Alien attack

Uh oh! The aliens are planning an attack!
Colour in the dotted shapes to find out
which planet they plan to strike.

Holiday halves

I've been on so many holidays I can't remember where I've visited!
Fill in the badges with the names of all the places I've been by joining two word halves from below.

NCE

IL

CAN

FRA

ENG

ADA

AUST

ANY

AICA

GERM

BRAZ

MEX

ICO

JAM

RALIA

LAND

Perfect pairs

Each of these words has an opposite. Draw lines to join the pairs of opposite words.

SLOW

YOUNG

COLD

LIGHT

DRY

DIRTY

WET

TALL

FAST

HOT

HEAVY

SHORT

OLD

CLEAN

Missing toppings!

Each pizza topping has a number value from 1 to 5. Draw toppings onto slices 2, 3 and 4 to make the toppings on each slice add up to exactly the same number as slice 1.

Monster change

Dr Jangle drank a potion that turned him into Mr Hideous! Order the pictures from 1 to 9 to see the change.

copy street

Mr Mirror wants his house to look
exactly like his neighbour's.

He has everything he needs to
build it, but which **THREE** parts
does he **NOT** need?

?

This monster ate the menu!

Cross out all letters that appear twice, then unscramble the rest to see what he's ordered.

J M U S
C A E J
C k M U
U S

Now quickly draw it here - before he eats the table!

21

Happy

Birthday

23

Silly Circus

It's audition time at the
Superstar Circus! Can you find:

9 balls

9 yellow stars

8 saucers

6 hoops

10 cups

5 red noses

4 juggling pins

2 buckets

2 giant shoes

1 rabbit

Shadow Star

This singer is in the spotlight, but which shadow matches her exactly?

Penguin puzzle

Hop this little penguin home across the different shaped icebergs in this order:

You can go vertically or horizontally but not diagonally.

① ② ③ ④

Start!

Home →

Finish!

27

Bird spotting

Match these rare birds with their pictures in the bird-spotter's guide, then colour each with the correct pattern.

Bumble Jumble

Can you find Buzz? He's the only bee not part of a pair!

Odd robot out

Oops! There's a problem at the robot factory. Can you spot the robot that doesn't match?

Lost in space

Astronaut Aiden has forgotten where he parked his spaceship. Starting from Aiden, follow the arrows by the number of squares marked on each arrow to find the ship.

Start

Aiden

Example

find and squeak

START

FINISH

Ginger the cat has lost her favourite toy!
Guide her through the maze to find it.

32

Dotty dress

Join up the dot-to-dot to find out what's on the catwalk at this year's fashion show.

Then colour in my new outfit!

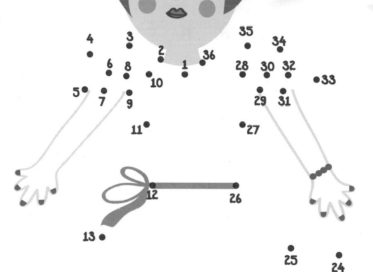

33

Brave cave explorers

This creepy cave is full of letters!

```
        B W T B R S T
    T S M I O O Z E L Y H D S
  S M E L L T W A E D I S P I D E R
  W K U F E H D R A M X G A R V
    W G C V I N C R E E P Y Q
    W S C A R E K D B P G
    H O W L D H R G R
    W E Q F N I E
        B S T R P
        B A T
        S
```

Find these words:

BAT	SCARE
BITE	SLIME
CREEPY	SLUG
DARK	SMELL
DRIP	SPIDER
HOWL	TOAD
OOZE	WEB

Costume calamity

Zap Man protects Super City from evil – but his costume is dirty! Which of these clean costumes is a replacement?

Science Explosion

The laboratory is disappearing!
Quick, write the number of the correct missing piece in each gap to fix it!

Who has been scrambled?

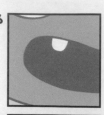

Copy each square into the correct section of the grid below to find out.

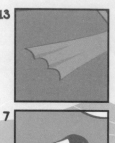
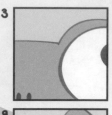
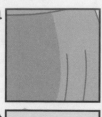
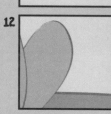

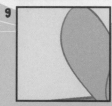

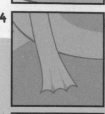

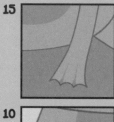
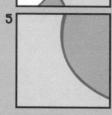

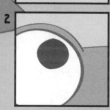
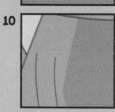

1	2	3	4
5	6	7	8
9	10	11	12
13	14	15	16

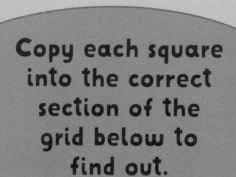

38

Pattern picker

What comes next in each pattern? Tick the box under each correct picture.

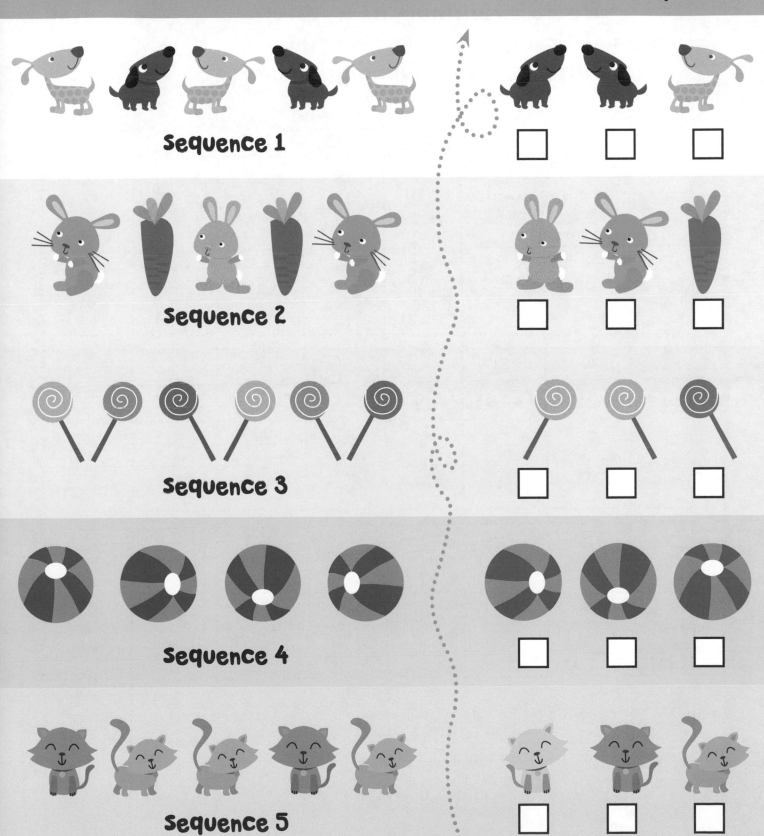

Sequence 1

Sequence 2

Sequence 3

Sequence 4

Sequence 5

four friends

We do everything as a group! Can you find us standing together in the crowded grid?

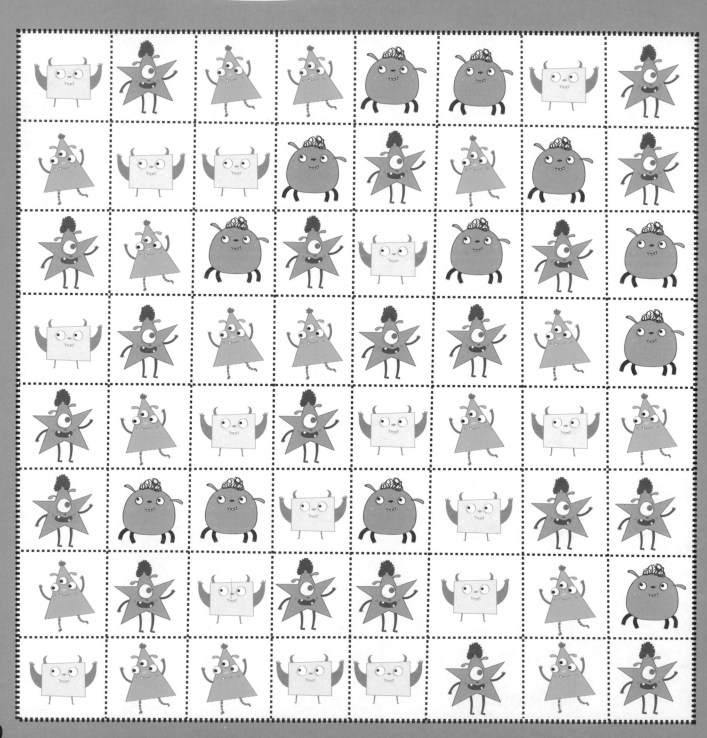

Number web

Spinderella
the spider loves to eat
flies! Fit the numbers into the
spaces in the grid so she can keep
track of how many
she's eaten.

43

48

258

354

426

2004

5886

6623

86564

6023568

9083157

Dance away

Hair grips

Apple

Dance shoes

Tights

Hairband

Purse

Comb

Leg Warmers

Water

Emily needs to pack a bag for her dance class. Look at the things she needs for one minute, then turn the page and see if you can remember them all!

Dotty dessert

Join the dots to reveal a delicious dessert!

63 62 61
65 55 54 53
64 52
66 60
67 57 56 38
68 59 58 39
69 42 41
46 45 43
70 51 37
47 44 40
49 50 36
48 26
28 27 35
29 33 34 25
1 30 31

32

2

20 18
21 17
19 23
3 22

16

12 10
13 11 9
4 15
14

5 8
6 7

43

odd one out

Clara loves collecting, but there is one thing that doesn't belong in each of her collections. Draw a circle around each odd one out.

2

1

3

4

What am I?

Which six different animals have been put together to create me? Label each of my parts with the name of the animal it came from.

Head ....

Wings

Nose

Tail

Body

Tongue

45

Secret formula

This experiment is nearly done! Which test tube will my secret formula end up in?

W x y z

seaside slices

It's a lovely day to be by the sea, but this sunny snap has been cut into slices! Work out the order it should be in, from left to right.

The correct order from left to right is:

H _ _ _ _ _ _ _ _

It's a jungle jumble!

Some of these amazing animals have never been seen before.

Which five creatures are not shown in the guide below?

Jewel journey

I've been given a new tiara for my birthday! Lead me to it by hopping across the gems in this order: ♦♦♦♦ Move forwards, backwards, up or down.

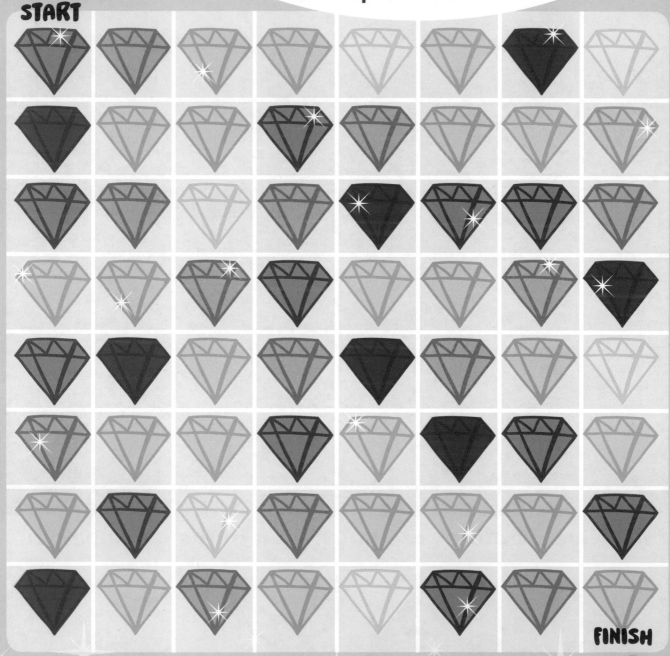

START

FINISH

50

Go fish

How many fish can you find in this tank?

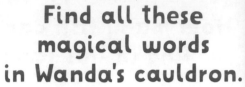

magic words

Find all these
magical words
in Wanda's cauldron.

BOIL	MAGIC
BROOM	SNAIL
CAT	SPELL
FROG	TRICK
GREEN	POTION
HAT	SPIDER

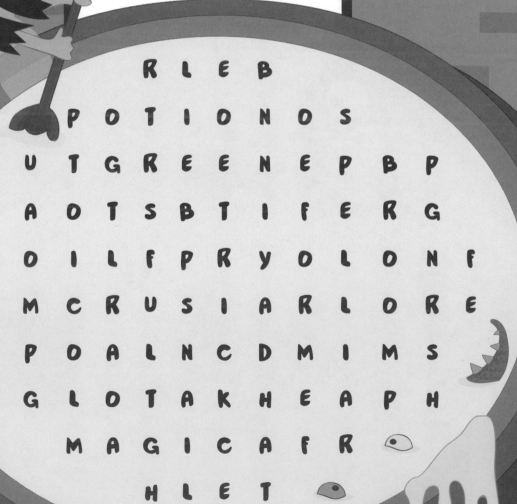

R L E B

P O T I O N O S

L U T G R E E N E P B P

N A O T S B T I F E R G

T B O I L F P R Y O L O N F

U I M C R U S I A R L O R E

S P O A L N C D M I M S

T G L O T A K H E A P H

M A G I C A F R

H L E T

Best bubbles

Which mermaid has blown the most bubbles?

....

Shelley

Coral

Marina

This mini-monster has a strange name:

MELLIFANGO

How many words can you make from it?

Write them all here.

1 ....
2 ....
3 ....
4 ....
5 ....
6 ....
7 ....
8 ....
9 ....
10 ....

11 ....
12 ....
13 ....
14 ....
15 ....
16 ....
17 ....
18 ....
19 ....
20 ....

How did you do?

0-5 words:
Shrunken brain!

6-10 words:
Monstrous mind!

11-15 words:
Scary smartypants!

16+ words:
Ghastly genius!

Bug hotel

Yikes! This room is full of creepy crawlies! How many times can you find the word BUG? Write your answer in the picture frame.

Don't forget it could be written forwards, backwards, up, down and diagonally!

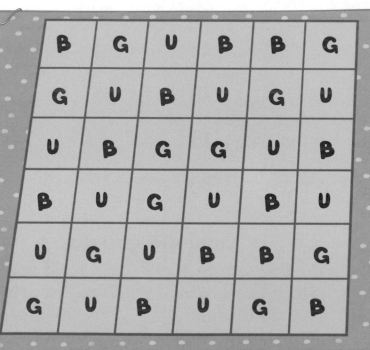

B	G	U	B	B	G
G	U	B	U	G	U
U	B	G	G	U	B
B	U	G	U	B	U
U	G	U	B	B	G
G	U	B	U	G	B

....

chimp challenge

These clever chimps have figured out how to reach the highest bananas. Work out what number is on each chimp by adding up the numbers on the two chimps below.

57

Double dance

These dancers are getting ready for the opening night!
Spot 10 differences in the bottom picture.

super spotting

It's playtime in the jungle, but which leopard has the most spots? Tick your answer!

A
B
C
D
E
F

Hide and seek

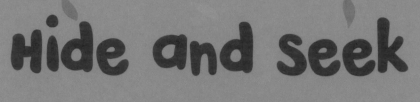

When no one is looking, the fairies come out to play! Can you work out where each of these photos was taken and then find the fairies hiding in the garden?

What do fairies like to eat?

Fairy cakes!

A new dinosaur fossil has been found. Join the dots to reveal the skeleton, then name your dino!

find a fossil

This is my

.................saurus!

slippy scarf

Everyone is making the most of the snow.
But which rabbit has left a scarf behind?
Follow the trails backwards to find out.

speedy snails

Which snail will race to the finish first? Find a friend and each get a pencil. Choose a snail each, then put your pencils on the start line. Race your pencils down the tracks to see who can lead their snail to the finish line first! Ready, set, GO!

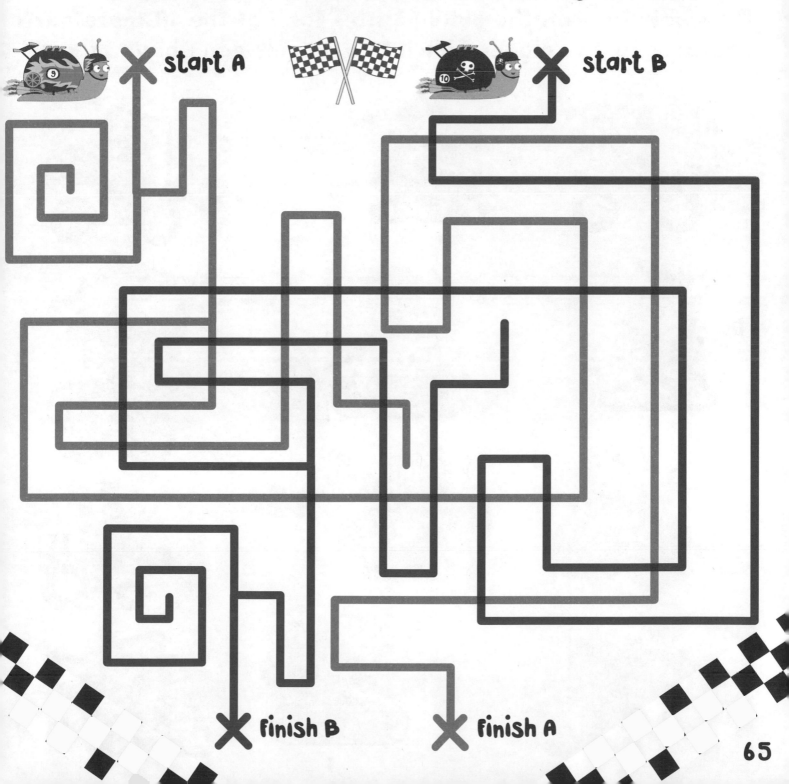

start A

start B

finish B

finish A

Digger repair

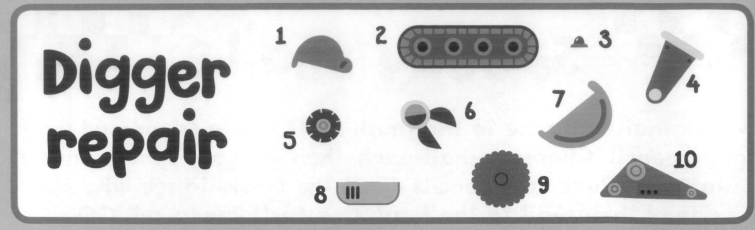

It's repair time on the building site! Each of the 10 spare parts belongs to one digger. Which two diggers don't have spares?

Big feast

- [ ] Bananas
- [ ] Apples
- [ ] Strawberries
- [ ] Pineapples
- [ ] Carrots
- [ ] Oranges

Gavin the grey bear loves all kinds of food. But what does he have the most of? Count the fruit in his dinner to find out.

chase the cheetah

Quick! Help us find the way to the speedy cheetah!

START

FINISH

Princess patterns

Princesses love to play number games!
Work out the missing numbers in each row.

A 14 | ___ | 10 | ___ | 6 | 4

B 5 | ___ | 15 | 20 | ___ | 30

C 1 | 2 | ___ | 8 | ___ | 32

D 1 | 2 | 4 | 7 | ___ | 16

Aztec Mystery

Professor Bingley is unlocking the secrets of Montenumba's Temple! Work out the numbers on each stone by adding up the numbers on the two stones below.

10   11

2   8   3   6   9

It might take years to crack this code!

Lost ballet shoes!

Can you help me find a route to the stage that passes every shoe without crossing back over my path? Then circle the shoe that's not part of a pair.

START

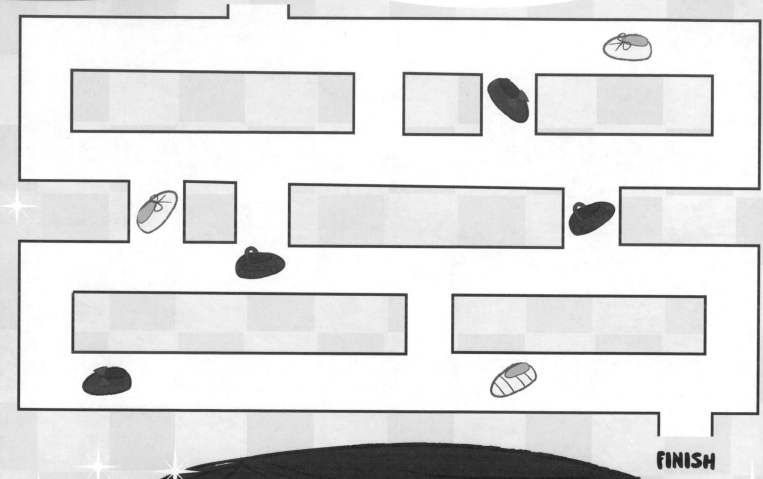

FINISH

party slip-ups

Something's wrong at the World Sports Championship.

Can you spot 12 things that aren't right in the stadium?

Duck crossing

These ducks don't like to get their feet wet!
Find a way across the river, using the even-numbered stones
only and without going backwards.

Shoppers!

Find and tick off all the items on the list.

77

- [ ] purple headphones
- [ ] light green shoes
- [ ] blue tie
- [ ] small orange handbag
- [ ] light blue backpack
- [ ] green scarf

Monster Munchies

Find a path through the food
following the above order
You can move one square at a time,
up, down and across, but not diagonally.

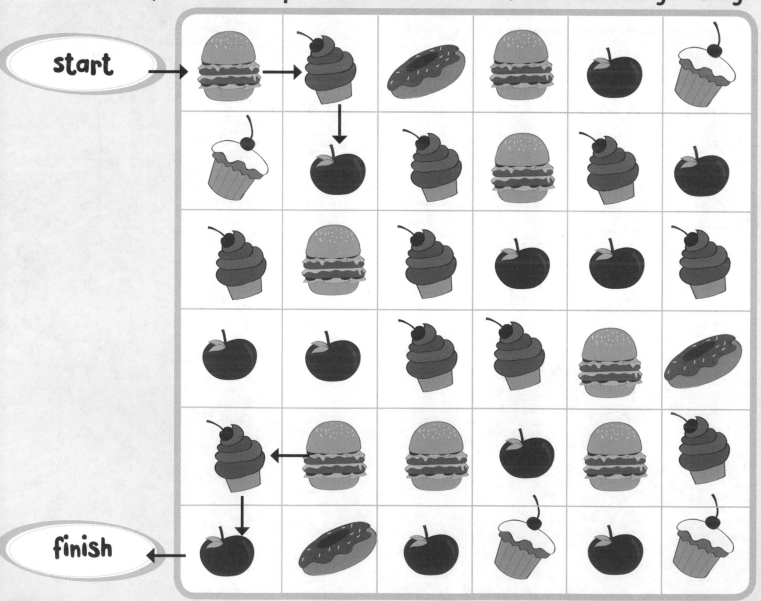

Buried treasure

Bella ballerina
What will Bella wear today?
Find the dress that matches her description.

Castle copy

King Norbert's castle has been smashed in a big battle. Rebuild it by copying one square at a time, using the numbers to help you.

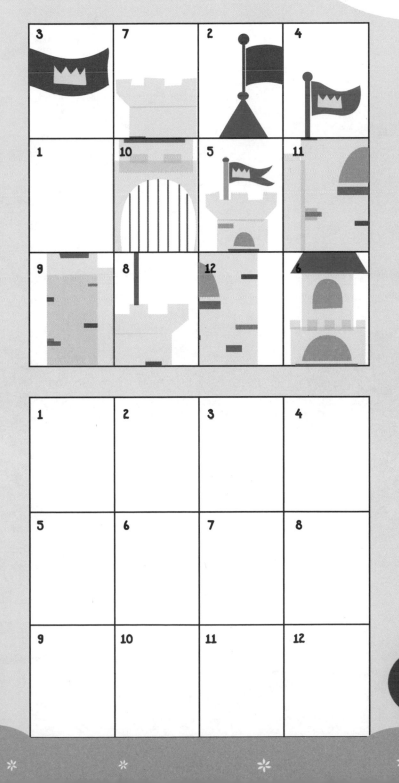

Dot-to-dot du!

Join the dots to reveal some wild haircuts.

82

Plane trails

Follow the trails behind each plane to spell the name of the countries they're flying to.

Justin's bedroom

Justin's bedroom is **SO** messy, he can't find his favourite toys and clothes! Can you?

Tick off the items as you find them.

- [ ] 9 felt-tip pens
- [ ] 7 toy cars
- [ ] 6 action figures
- [ ] 5 dinosaurs and prehistoric reptiles
- [ ] 4 pairs of shoes
- [ ] 2 toy helicopters
- [ ] 1 football

Robot xt-003

Circle five parts that are missing on this robot's right side.

Baker Gallery

Francis Baker is painting fakes of famous paintings, but he's not very good. Spot one mistake in each of his fakes.

original

Whale maze

Ben Barracuda has been accidentally swallowed by the whale.
Show him a way out of the whale's mouth so he can swim free.

forgetful freddy!

Where is Freddy's car?
It's slightly different to all the other models.

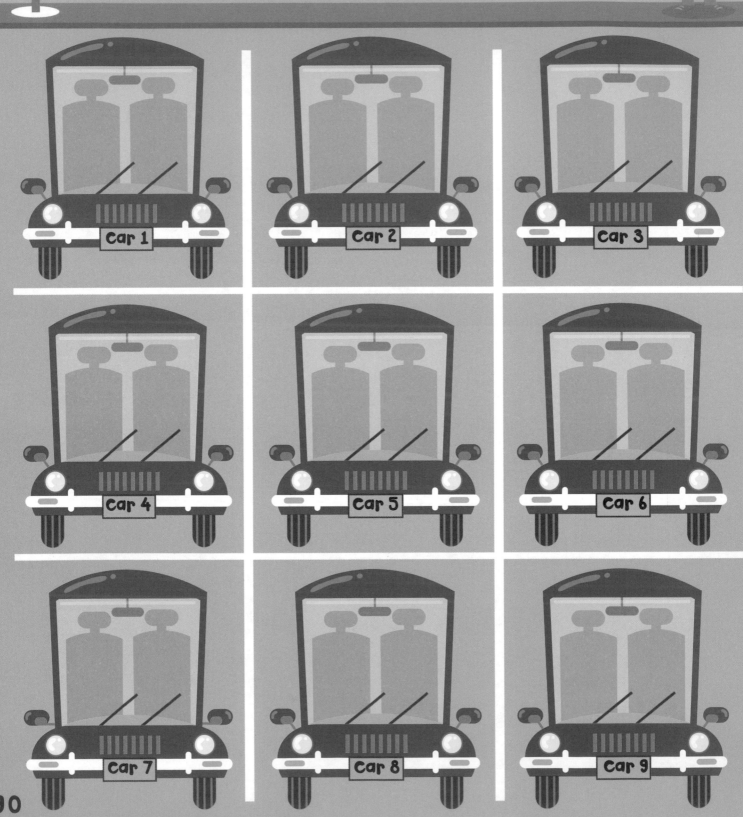

Crowded Bus

 30 MAX ⬡ SCHOOL BUS ⬡ **30 MAX**

Mason wants to get on the school bus but there are only 30 seats. Count the children already aboard to see if there is space for him.

Who caught the most fish?

fishing competition!

BELCHY

BRUISER

SLUGSTAIN

GREENSNOT

SLOBBER

Which weather?

Fog · **Sun** · **Ice** · **Wind** · **Snow** · **Rain**

Draw lines to match each item with
the right weather.

Purr-fect match

Match each white cat to the black cat
which has the same pattern.

DESTINATION	ANSWERS
S I P A R	
H N A G S N W I T O	
M O R E	
C O M O W S	
N L N O D O	
B U L I N D	

Unscramble each word to find out where each plane is flying. Use these stamps as clues if you need to!

PARIS FRANCE

MOSCOW

LONDON

ROME

WASHINGTON

DUBLIN IRELAND

95

Can you work out which dance move comes next?

97

Owl match

Tonight the trees are full of owls. Find all the matching pairs.

98

castle confusion

My castle is missing five pieces! Compare both sides then find five parts that are missing from the right-hand side.

Bug hunt

100

Space Search

Can you help the starship find all these words on the asteroids? Look up, down and across.

B R K C Q O O Z O V C A I O L N A C X V
V V E N U S M M S A T U R N S U B O C G
B A S Z T A A A E P O F G Y Z L V M S W
V C R S P A C E D J G X F U H H S E R B
Y P Z W E P F J L C H D M Y B T N T M U
O Q L M D V J P G X D E M Y V R E I O E
A U H S C F F L O V R U D P J A D Q O Q
V R T R R J D A G M U P Z W F E W U N L
E A Q A B I J N S V B L R E T J Y D Q H
H N U M R D W E Q N E P T U N E J S Z A
R U P R K P V T E P Q R Z B Y Q U U W J
H S J U P I T E R L V X S T A R A I H O

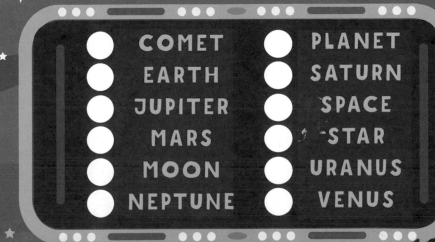

- COMET
- EARTH
- JUPITER
- MARS
- MOON
- NEPTUNE
- PLANET
- SATURN
- SPACE
- STAR
- URANUS
- VENUS

Toy box

We always stick together! Can you spot us sitting in this exact order in the toy box?

Dragon day

1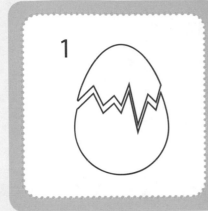

2

3

4

5

6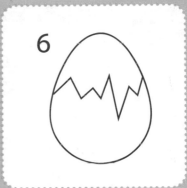

7

8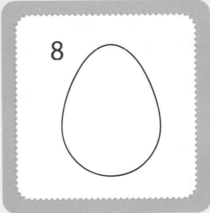

9

10

Mama Dragon's baby is hatching!
List the pictures in the
right order to show the baby
breaking free of his egg.

Egg _ _ _ _ _ _ _ _ _ _ Dragon

sail away

It's a beautiful day aboard the cruise ship! But can you find 9 differences in its reflection?

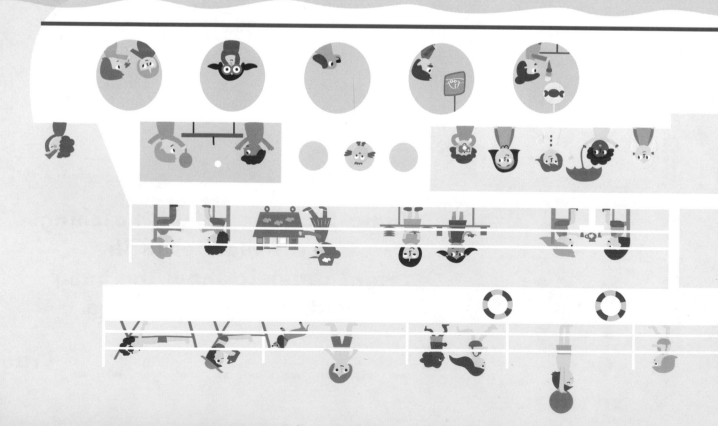

Ready to rock!

Which rock-star pieces fit into the concert scene? Write the letters in the spaces.

A

B

C

D

E

F

G

H

I

J

Butterfly beauties

106

There are

_____

pairs of butterflies.

sky high

Animal halves

Use the word parts from the bottom of the page to finish the zoo signs!

GOR_____

_____HANT

____KEY

SK____

__ON

____TURE

BO___

SCOR_____

LI

PION

VUL

MON

ELEP

UNK

ILLA

AR

Time out

Can you re-build Princess Ticktock's
grandfather clock from the broken parts?

Top ___ ___ ___ ___ ___ ___ bottom

Midnight magic

Where do all the missing pieces fit in this sleepy scene?

1.
2.
3.
4.
5.
6.
7.
8.

Missing Music

Which cello is mine? Match the silhouette to find out!

The instrument that matches is

Creepy Creature

Doops! I've magically mixed up these six creatures. Help me to work out what they were so I can change them back.

The creatures are:

1 ....
2 ....
3 ....
4 ....
5 ....
6 ....

fluched awa

START

Oops! Princess Jinx has dropped her favourite ring! Find a path through the plumbing to return it to her.

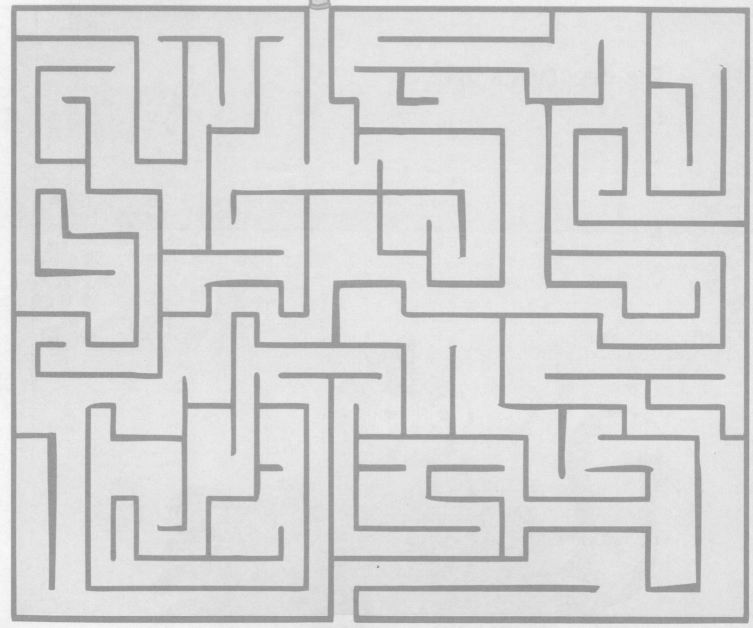

FINISH

which bike?

Read the descriptions to work out whose bike is whose!

MY BIKE IS NOT BLUE!

Jenny

MY BIKE DOES NOT HAVE A BASKET!

Alicia

MY BIKE HAS A BLACK SADDLE AND NO BASKET!

Emily

fairground fun

Fill in the blank spaces on the big wheel so that each pair of numbers joined through the middle adds up to 16.

Help us crack the safe! Fit the List of numbers into the grid below. The numbers in the red circles are the code!

Robber rats

15798
24598
32816
40134
46743
2540423
8743306

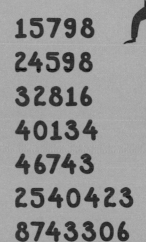

flower power

It's springtime in the park.
Find these three special flowers
in the colourful display:

Snip Snap

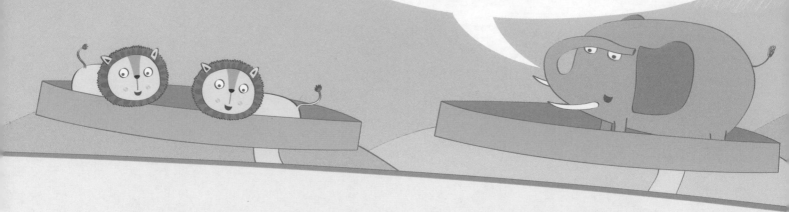

Who's new at the zoo?
finish the dot-to-dot to find out
and colour them in!

Answers

p4 - MATHS

p5

p6

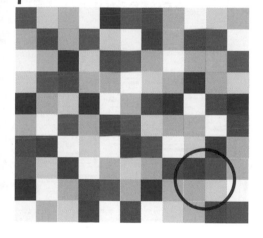

p8 - 3 green, 2 orange, 3 blue, 2 pink, 2 purple

p9

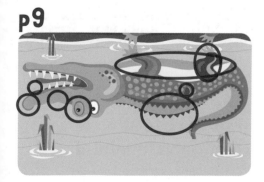

p10

6 + 6 = 12, 15 − 5 = 10, 6 + 3 = 9
12 − 5 = 7, 4 + 3 = 7

p11 - C6

p12 - 13

p14 - PLANET EARTH!

p15

AUSTRALIA   GERMANY
BRAZIL   MEXICO
CANADA   JAMAICA
ENGLAND   FRANCE

p16

SLOW and FAST
SHORT and TALL
LIGHT and HEAVY
WET and DRY
HOT and COLD
YOUNG and OLD
DIRTY and CLEAN

p17 - Slice 1 = 8. More than one way to make the other slices add up to 8.

p18

p19

p20-21 - The monster ordered CAKE.
You need to draw:
3 muffins, 3 cupcakes, 4 cookies.

p22-23

p24-25

p26 - Shadow D

p27

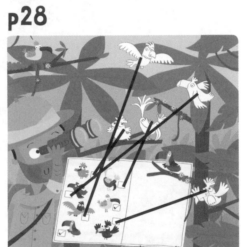

p28

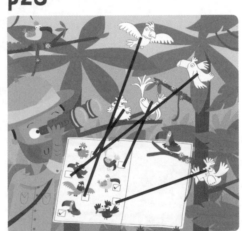

p29

p30 - Robot F

p31 - Spaceship C

p32

p33 - Your dot-to-dot should reveal a fashionable mini dress!

p34

```
        B W T B R S T
    T S M I O O Z E L y H D S
  S M E L L T W A E D I S P I D E R
    W K U F E H D R A M x G A R V
    W G C V I N C R E E P y Q
      W S C A R E K D B P G
      H O W L O D H R G R
      W E Q F N I E
        B S T R P
        B A T
```

p35 - Suit E

p36 - 37

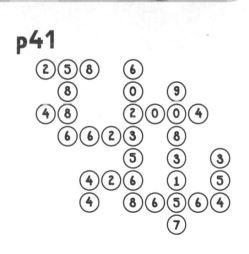

p38

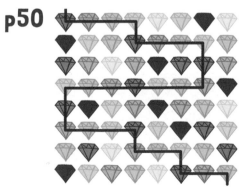

p39

1 (dog) 2 (carrot) 3 (lollipop)
4 (ball) 5 (cat)

p40

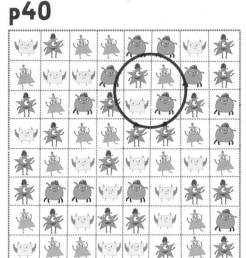

p41

```
2 5 8      6
  8      0    9
4 8      2 0 0 4
  6 6 2 3    8
      5    3    3
  4 2 6    1    5
  4    8 6 5 6 4
           7
```

p43 - Your dot-to-dot should reveal an icecream sundae!

p44

p45 - Head – lion; tail –scorpion; body – gorilla; tongue – snake; nose – elephant; wings – bat

p46 - Test tube X

p47 - H, C, F, B, G, D, A, I, E

p48 - 49

p50

p51 - 16 fish

p52

p53 - Coral blew 34 bubbles. Marina blew 19 bubbles. Shelley blew 15 bubbles. Coral blew the most bubbles.

p54 - ORANGE, APPLE, PEAR.

p55 - You could have:
AM, GO, IF, MA, NO, ON, AGE, FIN, FOG, ILL, LEG, LOG, MAN, MEN, OIL, FALL, FAME, FELL, FLAG, FLEA, FLOG, FOAM, FOIL, GAME, GOLF, GONE, LEAF, LIFE, LIME, LOAF, LONG, MALL, MEAL, MILE, MOLE, NAME, ANGEL, FLAME, FLING, GNOME, FLAMINGO.

p56 - The word BUG appears 22 times.

p57
48
20 28
8 12 16
3 5 7 9
1 2 3 4 5

p58

p59 - Leopard F

p60-61

p62 - Ship D

p63 - Your dot-to-dot should reveal a giant dino skeleton.

p64 - Rabbit E

p66 - C and H don't have spares

p67
6 bananas
5 apples
7 strawberries
5 pineapples
6 carrots
6 oranges

Strawberries are his favourite.

p68
A 14
B 21
C 11
D 15
E 05
F 12

p69

p70

A 14, 12, 10, 8, 6, 4
B 5, 10, 15, 20, 25, 30
C 1, 2, 4, 8, 16, 32
D 1, 2, 4, 7, 11, 16

p71

85
41 44
21 20 24
10 11 9 15
2 8 3 6 9

p72

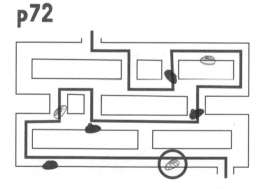

p73

p74-75

p76

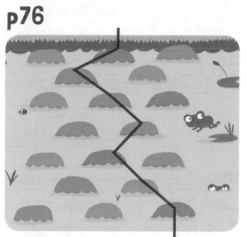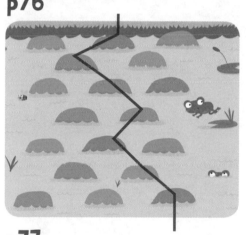

p77

p78

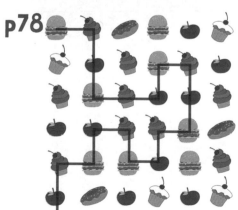

p79

p80

p81 - Your dot-to-dot should reveal one spiky hairstyle and one very tall hairpiece with a bow!

p83
1 Australia
2 Switzerland
3 Madagascar

p88

p90

p84 - 85

p86
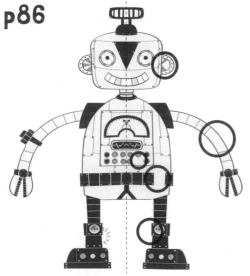

p87 - Track C

p89

p91 - There are 29 children so there is 1 space left for Mason.

p92 - Greensnot won with 15 fish.

p93 - Sun – sunglasses; rain – umbrella; wind – kite; snow – sledge; fog – torch; ice – ice-skates

p94